COLOR MY O...
HALLOWEEN STORY

AN IMMERSIVE, CUSTOMIZABLE COLORING BOOK FOR KIDS
(THAT RHYMES!)

BRIAN C HAILES

For information about permission to reproduce selections from this book, please write Permissions, Epic Edge Publishing, 1934 Fielding Hill Ln, Draper, UT 84020.

www.epicedgepublishing.com

Library of Congress Cataloging-in-Publication Data
Color My Own Halloween Story: An Immersive, Customizable Coloring Book for Kids (That Rhymes!)
Written by Brian C Hailes

p. cm.

Summary: Color My Own Halloween Story and Activity Book celebrates the spooky fun and excitement of the Halloween season by bringing ghosts, goblins, witches and fairies right onto your haunted doorstep and into your child's creative coloring hands! This is a unique, customizable and entertaining coloring experience, wherein your child can become the hero of their own story by filling in certain parts of the rhyming narrative. That means that your little creative can make every page in this coloring book into their very own adventure! This hands-on experience will rattle your bones with fun Halloween colors, characters, and a poetic tale that is sure to get you into the ghostly holiday spirit!

Calling all young ghouls, princesses, vampires and werewolves! Grab your pumpkins—I mean, crayons, pencils and markers. It's time to go trick-or-treating—after you color your very own Halloween story . . . Are you scared?

(Intended for children ages 6-12 . . . or all kids at heart)

1. Childrens—Halloween. 2. Childrens—Coloring Books
3. Childrens—Holiday Activity Books
II. Hailes, Brian C., ill. III. Title.

Paperback ISBN-13: 978-1-951374-27-3
Hardback ISBN-13: 978-1-951374-30-3

Printed in the USA
Designed by Epic Edge Publishing

10 9 8 7 6 5 4 3 2 1

"When werewolves go howling and vampires are seen, the scarecrows and pumpkins chant, It's Halloween!"

— B.C. Halles

COLOR MY OWN
HALLOWEEN STORY

AN IMMERSIVE, CUSTOMIZABLE COLORING BOOK FOR KIDS
(THAT RHYMES!)

STARRING: _____
(your name)

Twilight comes, the air turns chill,

Costumed boys and girls emerge;

_____ , witches, ghosts and ghouls
(Your favorite costume)

Onto the streets, converge.

Laughing with their bags and pails,

On the hunt for candy sweet;

A shortcut through the graveyard . . .

Hey, it's time to trick-or-treat!

Angels, demons, wolves, the dead,
Approach your doorstep now;
And best be generous with your spoils;
Upon the hordes, endow!

Time and creativity
Have transformed every child;
They, with their cuteness, charm and _____
(magic, voodoo or trickery)
Cast their spells meant to beguile.

Warily, you pass the

Haunted mansion down the street,

Not quite sure it's worth the risk . . .

Engage? Or call retreat?

A light's on, and that means that

They're expecting you to come;

But once you make it to the _____ ,
(door, porch or mat)

It will be too late to run.

For waiting just inside could be

A man with sharp _____ eyes,

(your eye color)

With fangs and wings like bats',

Ill, undead brides in fair disguise.

A vampire like that Dracula,

Who sucks his victims' blood;

Who disappears in mirrors;

Drops dry corpses in the mud.

But why should _____ need to fear?
(princes, firemen or musketeers)

Or maidens good and kind?

Surely, bad things could not befall

The righteously inclined.

It's about bravery and courage;

Evil never wins the day.

They say the good guys always win,

It's true . . . Or do they?

AARGH! Pesky landlubbers beware,

Pirates nigh control these waters.

Avast ye, we'll steal your _____ ,
(booty, loot or candy)

Take yer sons, and chase yer daughters.

Ahoy, me Hearties, take their coffers!

Batten down the hatches.

Pillage, plunder, ransack, aye,

'Fore the Red Ensign dispatches!

King Tut's tomb has opened;

There are mummies on the loose!

Do not let them find you,

Or you'll wish you had the noose.

Their bandages won't save you

From their awful, _____ smell.
(putrid, stinky or reeking)

And if they catch you, with the dead,

Forever, you shall dwell.

The night is halfway over,

But the fun is just beginning;

Around the block and to and fro,

Our sugar-filled heads are spinning!

So grab your broomsticks, pom-poms;

Mermaids, sing your sweetest song;

The witching hour approaches;

Keep the _____ going strong!
(treating, fun times or
festivities)

On the mountain, near the forest,

Something howls up at the moon;

A coyote, wolf or werewolf?

Nothing else can hold that tune!

You'd better watch the shadows,

Listen close upon the breeze;

You never know just what could _____

(spring, bound or pounce)

From behind the limbs of trees.

The pumpkin patch is glowing,

Jack-o'-lanterns carved up nice,

With _____ faces, grimaces.
(clowny, happy or silly)

On the wind, sweet pumpkin spice.

What's that sound? That moaning?

Singsong voices in the air?

It's as if the choirs of angels

Used their nighttime prayers to scare.

The spirit of a warrior

Glides there across your path;

A samurai with katana,

And a caged up, hidden wrath;

Skilled in the art of _____ ,
(war, swordplay or swordsmanship)

She searches calmly for her mark;

Wrapped inside her kimono,

She keeps a deadly, vengeful spark.

The crows are out, and ravens,

Heralding the cry of death;

Something's happened, someone's hurt

Someone somewhere's out of breath . . .

The piper's paid, the bucket's kicked,

And Judgment Day's arrived;

It's time to face the _____ ;
(music, devil or curtains)

Look across that great divide.

The Ghost of Christmas Future's

Become the Ghost of Halloween;

And they seem quite contented

Just to stand there and watch me scream.

I am only _____ years old.
(your age)

How could this come to pass?

I'm too young to go to rest

Six feet under the grass.

WHEW! I'm back. Dream? Prank? Or nightmare?

You know, it's really hard to say.

The King of Terrors will have to wait;

For now, I'm here to stay.

And while I stay, let's have a party.

Let's celebrate the dead;

All those lovely, _____ souls
(lively, cheerful or kooky)

That have made the earth their bed.

Our party rages on and right

Into the dark, wee hours;

This one night of the year,

We acknowledge creepy, fiendish powers.

Next year, I will be a _____ ,
(next year's costume)

And I'll really steal the show;

It's Halloween! So boys and girls,

Let your imaginations flow!

UNTIL NEXT YEAR . . .

THE END

OTHER "COLOR MY OWN" TITLES
NOW AVAILABLE!

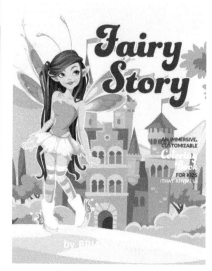

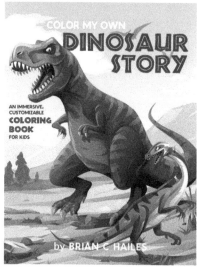
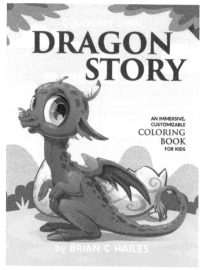
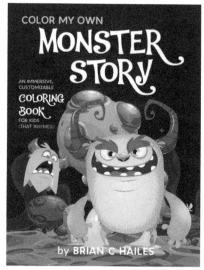

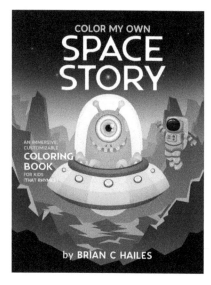

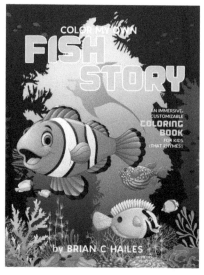

ABOUT THE AUTHOR

BRIAN C HAILES, creator of Draw It With Me (www.drawitwithme.com), is also the award-winning writer/ illustrator of over forty-five (and counting) novels, children's picture books, comics and graphic novels, including Blink: An Illustrated Spy Thriller Novel, Devil's Triangle, Dragon's Gait, Skeleton Play, Don't Go Near the Crocodile Ponds, If I Were a Spaceman, Here, There Be Monsters, Heroic, Passion & Spirit, Continuum (Arcana Studios), as well as McKenna, McKenna, Ready to Fly, and Grace & Sylvie: A Recipe for Family (American Girl), among others. In addition to his publishing credits, Hailes has also illustrated an extensive collection of fantasy, science fiction, and children's book covers as well as interior magazine illustrations. Hailes has received numerous awards for his works from across the country, including Winner of the L. Ron Hubbard Illustrators of the Future contest out of Hollywood. His artwork has also been featured in the 2017-2020 editions of Infected By Art.

Hailes studied illustration and graphic design at Utah State University where he received his Bachelor of Fine Arts degree, as well as the Academy of Art University in San Francisco.

He currently lives in Salt Lake City with his wife and four boys, where he continues to write, paint and draw regularly. More of his work can be seen at HailesArt.com

Other Titles Available from
Epic Edge Publishing

Illustrated Novels	Graphic Novels / Comics	Childrens Picture Books	Anthologies	Non-Fiction

Blink: An Illustrated
Spy Thriller Novel
by Brian C Hailes

Devil's Triangle:
The Complete
Graphic Novel
by Brian C Hailes
& Blake Casselman

If I Were a Spaceman:
A Rhyming Adventure
Through the Cosmos
by Brian C Hailes
& Tithi Luadthong

Cresting the Sun: A Sci-fi
/ Fantasy Anthology
Featuring 12 Award-
Winning Short Stories
by Brian C Hailes,
Rick Bennett
& Nicholas Adams

Draw It With Me: The
Dynamic Female Figure
(Available 2020!)
by Brian C Hailes

Avila
(Available 2021!)
by Robert J Defendi
& Brian C Hailes

Dragon's Gait
by Brian C Hailes

Here, There Be Monsters
by Brian C Hailes
& Tithi Luadthong

Heroic: Tales of the
Extraordinary
by Blake Casselman,
David Farland,
Michael Stackpole
& more

DIWM 2020 Annual 1
(Available 2020!)
by Brian C Hailes,
Heather Edwards
& more

Don't Go Near the
Crocodile Ponds
by Brian C Hailes

KamiKazi
by John English
& Brian C Hailes

Skeleton Play
by Brian C Hailes

Passion & Spirit: The
Dance Quote Book
by Brian C Hailes

Can We Be Friends?
by Edie New
& Cindy Hailes

CPSIA information can be obtained
at www.ICGtesting.com
Printed in the USA
LVHW050202081020
668276LV00004B/121

9 781951 374303